A GARDENER'S
JOURNAL

Jacques Le Moyne (*c.* 1533-88) is arguably one of the finest botanical illustrators of the sixteenth century. Inspired by a love of nature, Le Moyne's drawings are meticulous in their depiction of detail, be it the shell of a snail or the stem of a rose. In addition to his draughtsmanship, Le Moyne also wrote poetry to accompany his watercolour drawings. An album of Jacques Le Moyne's drawings which includes the sonnet overleaf is housed in the Prints and Drawings Department in the British Museum.

CABBAGE ROSE, ROSA CENTIFOLIA
Watercolour and bodycolour within a ruled, red ink border,
213 x 140mm. Prints and Drawings Department,
P&D 1962-7-14-1(23)

THE BRITISH MUSEUM

A GARDENER'S

JOURNAL

Discordant harmony and balanced movement,
Winter and Summer, Autumn, reborn Spring,
Renewing her sweet scents and colouring,
Join in the praise of God's unfailing judgement.

This loving God gives every argument
To look for zeal from each created thing,
To bless His Name eternally and sing
All He has made in earth and firmament.

Above all He made man with head held high
To watch each morning as new light arrives
And decorates earth's breast with varied flowers.

There is no fruit, or grain, or grub, or fly
That does not preach one God, the least flower gives
Pledge of a Spring with everlasting colours.

JACQUES LE MOYNE, 1585

CONTENTS

SPRING

MAYFLOWER AND MEADOW BROWN BUTTERFLY
Hawthorn (Mayflower) with white flowers and pink stamens.
Watercolour and bodycolour within a ruled, red ink border,
216 x 140mm. Prints and Drawings Department,
P&D 1962-7-14-1(10)

9

Garden Plan

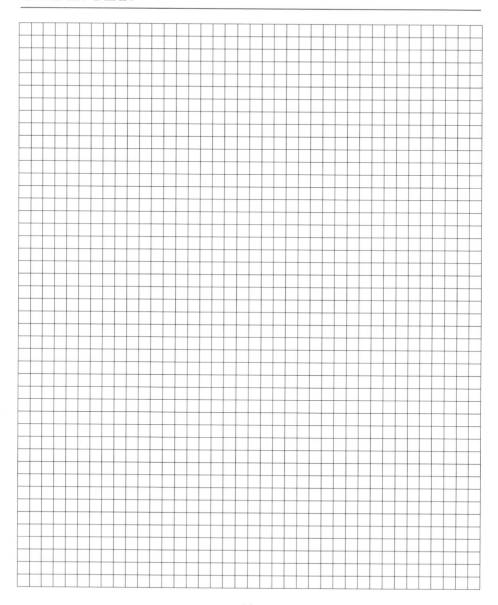

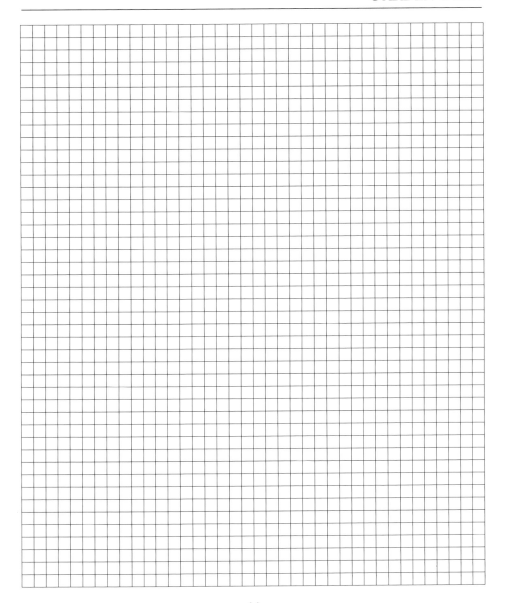

24

EVENT REMINDER

EVENT

DATE

COLUMBINE AND LADYBIRD Fully opened flowers of deep blue, stamens thick with yellow pollen. Watercolour and bodycolour within a ruled, red ink border, 213 x 144mm. Prints and Drawings Department, P&D 1962-7-14-1(22)

25

*STRAWBERRY Hautbois strawberry (Fragaria moschacrimson fruit and white flowers. Watercolour o
*

114-1(12)

GARDEN PLAN

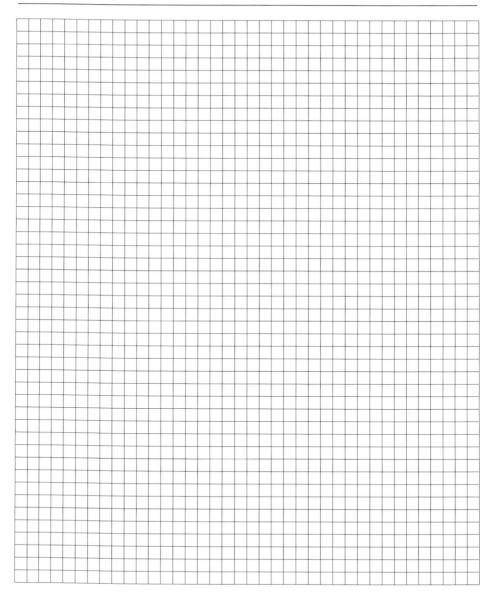

EVENT REMINDER

EVENT   DATE

_____   _____

_____   _____

_____   _____

_____   _____

_____   _____

_____   _____

_____   _____

_____   _____

_____   _____

_____   _____

_____   _____

_____   _____

_____   _____

_____   _____

_____   _____

_____   _____

Pot Marigold and Green-Veined White Butterfly
Double flower heads are orange to yellow in shade. Watercolour
and bodycolour within a ruled, red ink border, 207 x 145mm.
Prints and Drawings Department, P&D 1962-7-14-1(19)

33

OAK AND DRAGONFLY   *Probably a male dragonfly (Aeshna cynea) on Pedunculate Oak (Quercus robur). Watercolour and bodycolour within a ruled, red ink border, 213 x 142mm. Prints and Drawings Department, P&D 1962-7-14-1(35)*

GARDEN PLAN

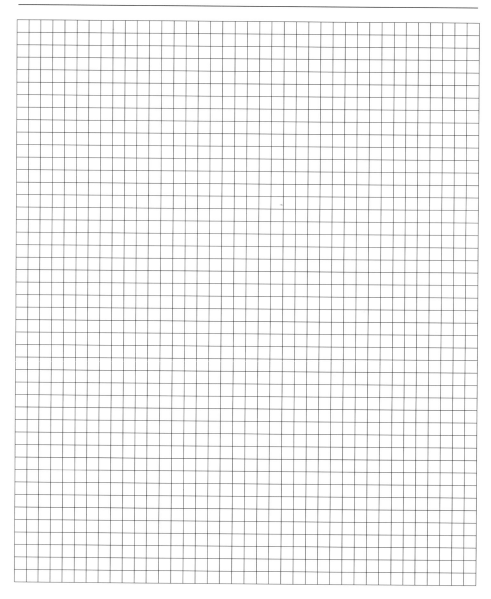

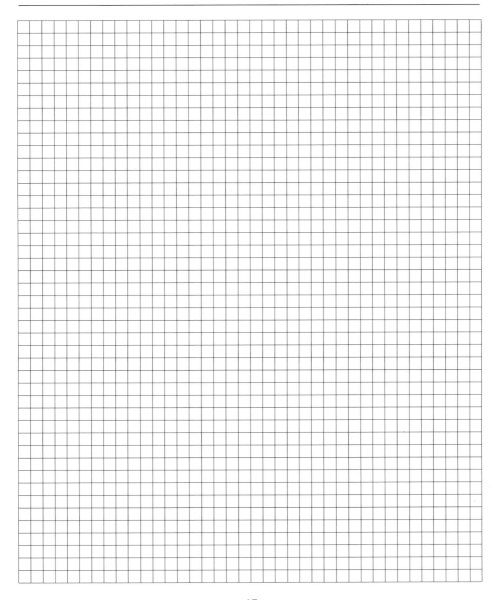

EVENT REMINDER

EVENT

DATE

GILLIFLOWER AND PRIVET HAWK MOTH   Stock (Matthiola incana) with privet hawk moth (Sphinx ligustri). Watercolour and bodycolour within a ruled, red ink border, 215 x 140mm. Prints and Drawings Department, P&D 1962-7-14-1(18)

WINTER

THISTLE AND DRAGONFLY   Milk thistle or St Mary's thistle
(Silybum marianum) and dragonfly. Watercolour and bodycolour
within a ruled, red ink border, 214 x 141mm.
Prints and Drawings Department, P&D 1962-7-14-1(27)

GARDEN PLAN

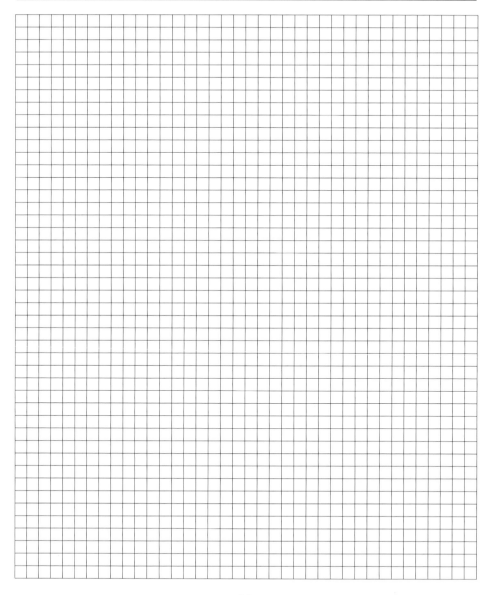

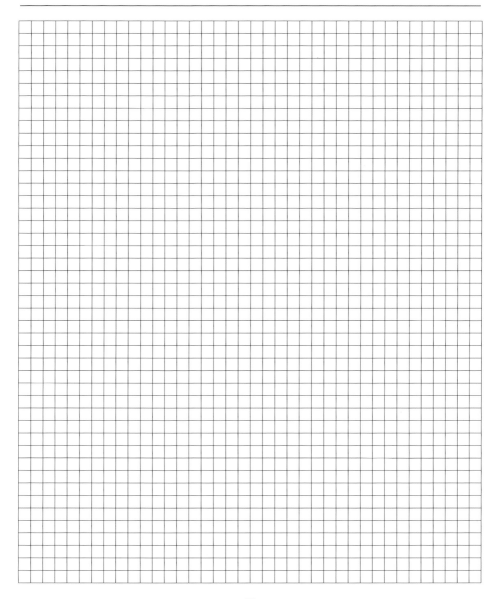

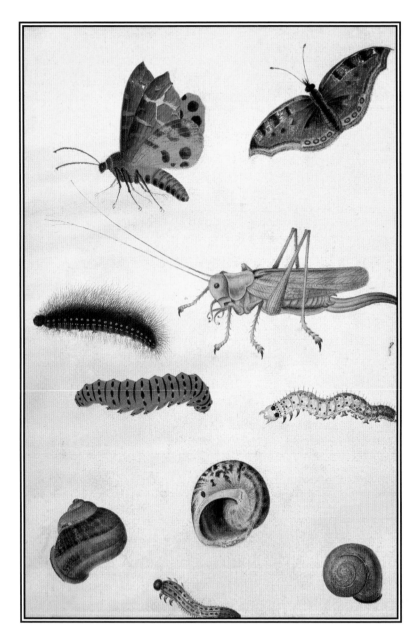

EVENT REMINDER

EVENT   DATE

STUDY OF INSECTS AND SHELLS Tiger moth, Tortoiseshell butterfly, Great Green Bush cricket, caterpillars of Swallow-tail butterfly and Leopard moth, three snail shells and larva of a Sawfly. Watercolour and bodycolour within a ruled, red ink border, 212 x 140mm. Prints and Drawings Department, P&D 1962-7-14-1(2)

80

Plant List

Common Name

Latin Name

_____ _____

_____ _____

_____ _____

_____ _____

_____ _____

_____ _____

_____ _____

_____ _____

_____ _____

_____ _____

_____ _____

_____ _____

_____ _____

_____ _____

_____ _____

_____ _____

_HEARTSEASE AND LARGE WHITE BUTTERFLY Deep red Wild
Pansy (Viola tricolor) and butterfly (Pieris brassicae). Watercolour
and bodycolour within a ruled, red ink border, 214 x 143mm.
Prints and Drawings Department, P&D 1962-7-14-1(17)_

COMMON NAME   LATIN NAME

COMMON NAME   LATIN NAME

COMMON NAME

LATIN NAME

COMMON NAME

LATIN NAME

GARDENS TO VISIT

SUPPLIERS: NURSERIES

NAME	ADDRESS	PHONE/WEBSITE

NAME   ADDRESS   PHONE/WEBSITE

SUPPLIERS: GARDEN FURNITURE

NAME	ADDRESS	PHONE/WEBSITE

NAME	ADDRESS	PHONE/WEBSITE

SUPPLIERS: SERVICES

NAME	ADDRESS	PHONE/WEBSITE

NAME   ADDRESS   PHONE/WEBSITE